BABY

From the very first moment,
we loved you
with all our hearts.

_____

baby's full name

_____

birthdate

WAITING
FOR YOU

What happy thoughts did the two of you talk about before I arrived? Describe any dreams you had before I was born. What thoughts made you look forward to my birth?

You have always been in our thoughts and dreams even before you were born.

How did you plan my birth? What changes did you make in your lives before I arrived?

Before your birth we imagined a future with you.

place baby shower invitation

place photo from baby shower

YOUR ARRIVAL

Tell me the story of my birth...

A radiant miracle in our lives...is you.

Provide the loving details of how I looked at birth. Height, weight, hair color, eye color. What was the most amazing trait I possessed at birth?

Holding you for the first time we felt a deep, never known love.

Place birth certificate or
birth announcement here

place first photos of me

place first photos of me

WELCOME HOME

What happened on our first day home together? How did I surprise you?

We touch tiny fingers and tiny toes with hearts overflowing with joy.

Who honored our family with favors and food while we rested at home?
What were you most grateful for in the first days of my life?

The kindness of others helped us to care for you in those early days.

Who stopped by to visit me after I was born? What were their thoughts when they met me? Write down any gifts that were given to me.

Many who waited for you came to visit with treasures and gifts.

place photo

place photo

What world events are happening today? Who are the famous people who share my birthday?

At your birth you became part of this big, beautiful world.

Describe the home we are living in right now. How did you prepare my nursery? Where do I sleep?

We nestled you into our home and covered you with our love.

What significant details do you notice about me after a few days of life?
What habits do I already have? How do you know when I am happy?
What makes me sad?

Tiny eyes watch and wait, tiny ears listen.

place photo

ALL ABOUT YOU

What can I do now that wasn't possible at birth? What surprises have awakened you to notice my development? Describe the first time I rolled over, held up my head, sat up, crawled, stood up, and walked.

Amazing how your little body can master so many new things.

When was my first smile? My first bath? My first kiss? My first time to drink from a cup? Write down stories that happened during these first events.

Show us your world, how fast you grow, how much you know.

When did I first talk? What were my first words? Remember to record translations and dialects of the words I first spoke. Do I have any pet names for favorite objects?

How do I play? What are my favorite games? What makes me laugh?

Innocence shows us how to live in the moment of life.

What do we enjoy doing outdoors together? How do I respond to being outside?

Sun, moon and sky send their greetings to you, little child.

Tell a story about a favorite trip we took together. What kind of traveler am I?

Everywhere we go is an adventure with you.

What were the doctor's comments during my check-ups? Record my growth for each visit. Anything else you want to remember?

We cared for you and guided your health with a watchful heart.

place photo

place photo

YOUR
FAMILY

What do we do as a family? Do we have any family rituals? How have I enriched our family life?

Where there were just two, now there is a family.

Tell the story of the first meeting between my siblings and me. Record their comments and questions on this page.

For the rest of their lives brothers and sisters will keep family moments in their hearts.

Describe any other family members who care about me. How have they made themselves a part of my life?

Someday you will find yourself amidst the dear people we call family.

How have we stayed in touch with distant relatives since I was born?
How have these same relatives corresponded with me?

Across many miles we send our warm hugs and nuzzled noses.

Tell a story about making friends. Who are my friends?
Where do we get together?

Friends provide the moments where we look back and smile.

Use this page to record my very own family tree.

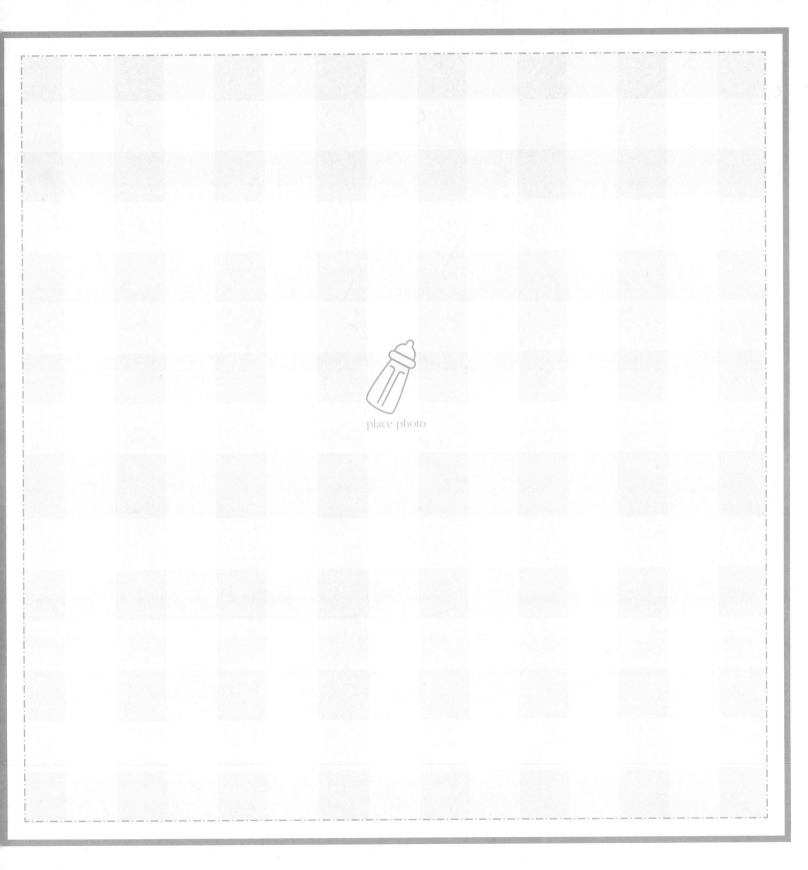
place photo

FIRSTS

How would you describe my personality at one year? What have you come to know about me as this year has passed?

In the blink of an eye you have changed, already we understand who you are.

How will you celebrate my first birthday? What beloved moments are you reminiscing about?

Our lives are filled with garlands of love, bouquets of hope, and baskets of gratefulness.

attach an envelope with a lock of hair

What hopes and dreams do you have for me?

We listen with our hearts as we plan for your future.

What are your thoughts of this past year with me? How have I brought new insights to your life? How have we all grown since becoming a family?

We treasure our gift of time with you as we look back on this wondrous year.

place photo

place photo

Well Baby

Pediatrician

Visiting the Doctor

First Illness

Allergies

Comments

DOCTOR VISITS

Date   Reason for Visit

FIRST HANDPRINT

First Footprint

GROWTH CHART

Date	Age	Height	Length	Weight

IMMUNIZATIONS

Shot	Date	Age

FIRST TEETH

First Tooth Appeared

Second Tooth Appeared

Others Came

Teething Tips from Friends & Family

Tips to Remember

place photo

place photo

place photo

FIRST HOLIDAY

Tell me about my first Christmas. What memories do you want to savor of this time?

The simple gifts of life, love and laughter are all we need with you.

place photo

place photo

© 2002 Havoc Publishing
San Diego, California
U.S.A.

Text by Maureen Webster

ISBN 0-7416-1939-3

www.havocpub.com

Made in China